Specific Skill Series

Locating the Answer

Richard A. Boning

Fifth Edition

SRA/McGraw-Hill

Columbus, Ohio

Cover, Back Cover, ZEFA/Germany/ The Stock Market

SRA/McGraw-Hill

A Division of The **McGraw·Hill** *Companies*

Send all inquiries to:
    SRA/McGraw-Hill
    250 Old Wilson Bridge Road, Suite 310
    Worthington, OH 43085

ISBN 0-02-687953-0

    5 6 7 8 9 IMP 00 99

To the Teacher

PURPOSE:

As its title indicates, LOCATING THE ANSWER develops pupils' skill in finding *where* sought-for information can be found within a passage. Pupils must carefully read and understand each question, grasp phrase and sentence units, and discriminate between pertinent and irrelevant ideas.

FOR WHOM:

The skill of LOCATING THE ANSWER is developed through a series of books spanning ten levels (Picture, Preparatory, A, B, C, D, E, F, G, H). The Picture Level is for pupils who have not acquired a basic sight vocabulary. The Preparatory Level is for pupils who have a basic sight vocabulary but are not yet ready for the first-grade-level book. Books A through H are appropriate for pupils who can read on levels one through eight, respectively. **The use of the *Specific Skill Series Placement Test* is recommended to determine the appropriate level.**

THE NEW EDITION:

The fifth edition of the *Specific Skill Series* maintains the quality and focus that has distinguished this program for more than 25 years. A key element central to the program's success has been the unique nature of the reading selections. Nonfiction pieces about current topics have been designed to stimulate the interest of students, motivating them to use the comprehension strategies they have learned to further their reading. To keep this important aspect of the program intact, a percentage of the reading selections have been replaced in order to ensure the continued relevance of the subject material.

In addition, a significant percentage of the artwork in the program has been replaced to give the books a contemporary look. The cover photographs are designed to appeal to readers of all ages.

SESSIONS:

Short practice sessions are the most effective. It is desirable to have a practice session every day or every other day, using a few units each session.

To the Teacher

SCORING:

Pupils should record their answers on the reproducible worksheets. The worksheets make scoring easier and provide uniform records of the pupils' work. Using worksheets also avoids consuming the exercise books.

It is important for pupils to know how well they are doing. For this reason, units should be scored as soon as they have been completed. Then a discussion can be held in which pupils justify their choices. (The Integrated Language Activities, many of which are open-ended, do not lend themselves to an objective score; thus there are no answer keys for these pages.)

GENERAL INFORMATION ON *LOCATING THE ANSWER*:

At the earlier levels the answer to the question is worded much the same as the question itself. As the books increase in difficulty, there is less correspondence between the phrasing of the question and the phrasing of the answer.

SUGGESTED STEPS:

1. Pupils read the question *first* and then look for the answer.

2. Pupils use the range finder (sentence choices) in Books B–H. The letters or numbers in the range finder (below the question) indicate which sentences must be read to locate the answer to the question. In the Picture Level, the pupils decide which picture answers the question. For Preparatory and A levels, the number before the question tells the paragraph to read.

3. Pupils read the sentences with the question in mind. (On the Picture Level, pupils look at the pictures. On the Preparatory and A levels, pupils read the paragraph.)

4. When using Books B–H, pupils write (in the space on the worksheet) the letter or number of the sentence that answers the question. On the Picture Level, pupils write the letter of the correct picture choice. On the Preparatory and A levels, pupils write the letter of the correct word choice.

Additional information on using LOCATING THE ANSWER with pupils will be found in the **Specific Skill Series Teacher's Manual**.

RELATED MATERIALS:

Specific Skill Series Placement Tests, which enable the teacher to place pupils at their appropriate levels in each skill, are available for the Elementary (Pre-1–6) and Midway (4–8) grade levels.

About This Book

Reading to find out about something is different from reading for other reasons. First you look for a page that will give you the answer you want. Then you read carefully. You think about what you want to find out.

Knowing what to look for when you read is important. You need to read with your questions in mind. It is like looking for something you have lost. You don't know where the lost thing is. But you know what you are looking for.

For each unit in this book, you will see a story and ten questions. The answers to the questions are in the story. Your job is to find **where** the answers are. You do not answer the questions. Instead, you tell which sentence gives the answer.

Read the sentences below. Find the sentence that answers this question: "Where do saltwater fish live?"

(**A**) There are two main groups of fish. (**B**) They are the saltwater fish and the freshwater fish. (**C**) Saltwater fish live in the oceans. (**D**) Freshwater fish live in streams, ponds, and lakes.

The answer is in sentence (**C**). Did you find it?

In each unit of this book, read the questions first. Look at the three letters below each question. Then look for the answer in the story sentences with those three letters. Read the sentences with the question in mind. Tell which sentence gives the answer.

(A) Potatoes were first grown by the Incas in Peru. (B) At first, most Europeans had little interest in this strange new plant from America. (C) They thought it was good only for feeding cattle. (D) Some people actually believed it was poisonous. (E) Now potatoes are grown in almost every country. (F) The value of the crop is great. (G) It is larger than the value of all the gold and silver discovered in the world each year!

(H) The potato is often called the white potato. (I) It is not a root like the sweet potato. (J) It is a swollen part of the stem and grows underground. (K) Most vegetables grow from seeds, but the potato does not. (L) It is grown from the bud or "eye" on the potato itself.

(M) Potatoes can be grown in almost any kind of soil. (N) On large farms they are planted by machine. (O) The machine places the "eyes" two to five inches deep. (P) If the soil is rich, they are planted close together. (Q) If it is not, they are spaced farther apart.

(R) Planting is done in May, and in October the potatoes are harvested. (S) Each plant produces from three to six potatoes. (T) In northern countries, potatoes produce more food per acre than any plant. (U) From each acre we get over 2,000 pounds of potatoes.

(V) Potatoes can be served at any meal. (W) They can be boiled, fried, or baked. (X) They are used to make alcohol and flour. (Y) One out of every six potatoes is used to make a special treat. (Z) It becomes potato chips!

1. Who grew the first potatoes?
   Sentence   **(A)**   **(B)**   **(C)**

2. What is the potato often called?
   Sentence   **(F)**   **(G)**   **(H)**

3. From what does the potato grow?
   Sentence   **(J)**   **(K)**   **(L)**

4. Can potatoes grow in almost any kind of soil?
   Sentence   **(K)**   **(L)**   **(M)**

5. How are potatoes planted on large farms?
   Sentence   **(M)**   **(N)**   **(O)**

6. When are potatoes planted close together?
   Sentence   **(O)**   **(P)**   **(Q)**

7. When is the planting done?
   Sentence   **(Q)**   **(R)**   **(S)**

8. How many potatoes are found on a plant?
   Sentence   **(R)**   **(S)**   **(T)**

9. Can potatoes be served at breakfast?
   Sentence   **(U)**   **(V)**   **(W)**

10. What special treat is made from potatoes?
    Sentence   **(X)**   **(Y)**   **(Z)**

(A) Many people shop in health food stores. (B) These stores sell some of the same foods that supermarkets do. (C) For example, health food stores sell fruits and vegetables. (D) Some health food stores also sell chicken, fish, and beef. (E) Grains, milk, and cheese can also be found in these stores.

(F) Health food stores try to get their products from farmers who do not use sprays to kill bugs on the food they grow. (G) Foods grown with no spraying are thought to be safer for people to eat.

(H) Health food stores also sell special packaged mixes. (I) People can buy vegetable-burger mix at health food stores. (J) People who don't want to eat meat use this kind of mix.

(K) Health food stores also sell vitamins and minerals. (L) Vitamins and minerals are usually sold in pill form. (M) Some people take these pills every day along with health foods. (N) Many people believe that vitamins and minerals will help them stay healthy.

(O) Some health food stores have juice bars. (P) There people can buy freshly made fruit and vegetable juices. (Q) Sometimes two or more juices are mixed in a drink. (R) One type of juice-bar drink is made with fresh carrots and apples.

(S) More and more people are shopping at health food stores. (T) These stores carry many kinds of products. (U) Products in health food stores may cost more than the same products in supermarkets. (V) But people who eat health foods say they feel better.

UNIT 2
Health Foods

1. Do health food stores and supermarkets sell some of the same foods?
   Sentence   **(A)**   **(B)**   **(C)**

2. Do some health food stores sell chicken?
   Sentence   **(C)**   **(D)**   **(E)**

3. From whom do health food stores try to get their products?
   Sentence   **(E)**   **(F)**   **(G)**

4. What kind of hamburger mix can you get at health stores?
   Sentence   **(G)**   **(H)**   **(I)**

5. In what form are vitamins and minerals usually sold?
   Sentence   **(J)**   **(K)**   **(L)**

6. How often do some people take vitamin and mineral pills?
   Sentence   **(L)**   **(M)**   **(N)**

7. What are vitamins and minerals supposed to do for people?
   Sentence   **(M)**   **(N)**   **(O)**

8. What can people buy at juice bars in health food stores?
   Sentence   **(O)**   **(P)**   **(Q)**

9. What is one type of juice sold at juice bars?
   Sentence   **(Q)**   **(R)**   **(S)**

10. May food cost more at a health food store than at a supermarket?
    Sentence   **(T)**   **(U)**   **(V)**

(A) Sugar comes mainly from two plants. (B) Most sugar comes from sugar cane. (C) Some comes from sugar beets. (D) Sugar from both plants looks and tastes the same.

(E) Sugar cane is a tall grass with a thick stalk and pointed leaves. (F) It is grown in a climate where there is warm sunshine and plenty of rain. (G) During the long growing season, the stalks fill with juice.

(H) When the cane is ready to be cut, the plants have become higher than a grown person. (I) To cut the crop, workers move through the fields swinging huge knives. (J) Machines are used for cutting in places where the ground is flat. (K) Leaves are stripped from the stalks right in the fields. (L) The cut stalks are loaded into railroad cars and are shipped to the sugar mill.

(M) At the sugar mill the cane is washed and cut into short lengths. (N) The juice squeezed from the cane is dark gray or green in color. (O) It is from this juice that sugar is made.

(P) Sugar beets are the second most important source of sugar. (Q) Unlike sugar cane, sugar beets do not require a lot of sun. (R) Sugar beets can also be grown in dry areas of the world.

(S) There is no such thing as waste where the modern sugar-beet grower is concerned. (T) Even the leaves from the tops of the sugar beets have their use. (U) The leaves are fed to the farm animals.

1. Sugar comes mostly from what plant?
   Sentence   **(A)**   **(B)**   **(C)**

2. Does sugar from both plants look alike?
   Sentence   **(C)**   **(D)**   **(E)**

3. Is sugar cane a grass?
   Sentence   **(E)**   **(F)**   **(G)**

4. Where is the juice found in sugar cane?
   Sentence   **(G)**   **(H)**   **(I)**

5. In what kind of places are machines used to cut the crop?
   Sentence   **(I)**   **(J)**   **(K)**

6. Where is the sugar cane washed?
   Sentence   **(K)**   **(L)**   **(M)**

7. What color is the juice taken from the cane?
   Sentence   **(M)**   **(N)**   **(O)**

8. Do sugar beets need a lot of sun?
   Sentence   **(O)**   **(P)**   **(Q)**

9. Do sugar beets need much rain?
   Sentence   **(Q)**   **(R)**   **(S)**

10. For what are sugar beet leaves used?
    Sentence   **(S)**   **(T)**   **(U)**

(**A**) Before farmers milk cows, they wash each cow's milk bag so that the milk will be clean. (**B**) Everything in the barns is kept spotless. (**C**) Inspectors visit the farms to see that all the health rules are obeyed.

(**D**) A cow gives milk for many months after she has had a baby calf. (**E**) Her milk bag, called an udder, is emptied twice a day every day of the year. (**F**) Milking times are around five o'clock in the morning and five o'clock at night.

(**G**) Farmers with a few cows milk them by hand. (**H**) On large dairy farms, milking machines are used. (**I**) These machines pump warm milk from the cows' udders into pails. (**J**) The milk is then put into large cans and stored in a cool place. (**K**) Farmers keep records of how much milk each cow gives. (**L**) Most cows give about twelve quarts of milk a day.

(**M**) Every day milk is taken from the farm in big tank trucks. (**N**) The milk is taken to a milk plant. (**O**) The milk plant is sometimes called a creamery. (**P**) Here, people smell, taste, and test the milk. (**Q**) This is to make sure that the milk is safe to drink or to be made into cheese, butter, or ice cream.

(**R**) All of the milk is pasteurized. (**S**) This means it is heated to kill germs. (**T**) Much milk is put into germ-free bottles. (**U**) The milk is then ready for delivery. (**V**) It is loaded onto trucks. (**W**) Much is sold to stores. (**X**) Some milk is sold to schools and hospitals. (**Y**) Other milk is sold to ice cream, butter, or cheese factories.

1. Why do farmers wash each cow's milk bag?
    Sentence   (**A**)   (**B**)   (**C**)

2. Does a cow give milk for a long time after giving birth to a calf?
    Sentence   (**C**)   (**D**)   (**E**)

3. How often is the milk bag emptied?
    Sentence   (**D**)   (**E**)   (**F**)

4. When is the milking done each day?
    Sentence   (**F**)   (**G**)   (**H**)

5. What does a milking machine do?
    Sentence   (**I**)   (**J**)   (**K**)

6. How much milk does one cow give in a day?
    Sentence   (**K**)   (**L**)   (**M**)

7. Where do tank trucks take the milk?
    Sentence   (**N**)   (**O**)   (**P**)

8. Is all the milk pasteurized?
    Sentence   (**Q**)   (**R**)   (**S**)

9. What does the heat do?
    Sentence   (**S**)   (**T**)   (**U**)

10. What kinds of factories buy milk?
    Sentence   (**W**)   (**X**)   (**Y**)

(A) Cheese can be made from any milk. (B) The people of Lapland make cheese from the milk of reindeer. (C) In the United States most cheese is made from cow's milk. (D) It takes about ten quarts of milk to make one pound of cheese.

(E) People have made cheese for thousands of years. (F) Some people make cheese in their homes, but most cheese is made in factories. (G) Milk is placed in large metal tanks, where it is allowed to sour. (H) As the milk sours, the solid parts separate from the liquid in white chunks. (I) These white chunks are called "curd." (J) The rest of the milk becomes thin and watery and is known as "whey."

(K) Both hard and soft cheeses are made mainly from the curd. (L) Hard cheeses contain very little whey. (M) Whey is pressed out of the cheeses by special pressing machines. (N) Hard cheeses form a covering on the outside. (O) This covering is called a rind, and it protects the cheese.

(P) Soft cheeses contain much more whey than do hard cheeses. (Q) Cottage cheese is a soft cheese. (R) Cream cheese, another soft cheese, is made by adding cream to cottage cheese. (S) Soft cheeses must be eaten soon, because they do not keep well.

(T) Much of the cheese sold in stores is called processed cheese. (U) Processed cheese is a mixture of different cheeses. (V) It is sold in bags and boxes. (W) These containers keep it from getting hard and protect the taste.

UNIT 5
From Milk to Cheese

1. Can cheese be made from milk?
    Sentence   **(A)**   **(B)**   **(C)**

2. How many quarts of milk does it take to make a pound of cheese?
    Sentence   **(C)**   **(D)**   **(E)**

3. Where is the milk put while it is turning sour?
    Sentence   **(E)**   **(F)**   **(G)**

4. What happens as milk gets sour?
    Sentence   **(G)**   **(H)**   **(I)**

5. What are the white chunks called?
    Sentence   **(I)**   **(J)**   **(K)**

6. Are cheeses made mainly from the curd or the whey?
    Sentence   **(K)**   **(L)**   **(M)**

7. How is the whey removed from the cheese?
    Sentence   **(M)**   **(N)**   **(O)**

8. What is the covering on the outside of cheese called?
    Sentence   **(O)**   **(P)**   **(Q)**

9. Is cottage cheese hard or soft?
    Sentence   **(Q)**   **(R)**   **(S)**

10. Is much processed cheese sold?
    Sentence   **(T)**   **(U)**   **(V)**

UNIT 6
Wheat to Flour

(**A**) Wheat is one of the world's most important foods. (**B**) It is from the fields of wheat that we get our daily bread. (**C**) Bread is made from the seeds of wheat that have been ground into flour.

(**D**) Before wheat is planted, the land must be plowed. (**E**) The plow breaks up large lumps of soil. (**F**) The finer the earth, the easier it is for the roots of the plant to spread through the soil. (**G**) The fields are then ready for seed. (**H**) A machine called a seeder plants the seeds in straight and even rows.

(**I**) When wheat changes from green to golden yellow, it is ripe. (**J**) Then the hard, dry grains are gathered. (**K**) To gather or harvest wheat, farmers use a machine called a combine. (**L**) This machine cuts the heads of wheat from the stalks. (**M**) In the heads of the stalks are the seeds that are made into flour. (**N**) The golden grain is poured from the combine into trucks.

(**O**) The grain is shipped to a grain elevator to be stored. (**P**) When sold, the grain is sent to a flour mill to be made into flour. (**Q**) At the mill the grain is cleaned and ground up finely. (**R**) Only the inside of the seed is used to make white flour. (**S**) Both the outside and the inside of the seeds are used to make dark wheat flour. (**T**) Machines pour the flour into large bags to be shipped to bakeries. (**U**) At bakeries some of the flour is made into rolls, cakes, and pies. (**V**) Most of the flour is made into bread.

1. Is wheat an important food?
   Sentence   **(A)**   **(B)**   **(C)**

2. Is wheat planted before the land is plowed?
   Sentence   **(C)**   **(D)**   **(E)**

3. What kind of earth is best for the roots?
   Sentence   **(E)**   **(F)**   **(G)**

4. Is ripe wheat a golden yellow?
   Sentence   **(H)**   **(I)**   **(J)**

5. What is used to gather the wheat crop?
   Sentence   **(J)**   **(K)**   **(L)**

6. Where do we find the seeds in the wheat plant?
   Sentence   **(L)**   **(M)**   **(N)**

7. Where is wheat stored?
   Sentence   **(N)**   **(O)**   **(P)**

8. Where is the grain cleaned?
   Sentence   **(P)**   **(Q)**   **(R)**

9. What is used to make the white flour?
   Sentence   **(R)**   **(S)**   **(T)**

10. Is most of the flour used to make bread?
    Sentence   **(T)**   **(U)**   **(V)**

You have read about potatoes, health foods, sugar, milk, cheese, and flour. If you had some questions about these words, you might be able to find the answers in a dictionary.

Dictionaries have certain types of information about words. Study the list below so you will know when to look in the dictionary for answers.

A dictionary—
- lists words in alphabetical, or ABC, order
- shows the spelling of words
- shows the different syllables, or parts, of words
- shows how to say words
- shows the meaning or meanings of words

A. Exercising Your Skill

Look in a dictionary for the word *tomato*. Write the numbers 1 through 5 on your paper. Write five things you learn about the word *tomato* in the dictionary. Use the list above if you need help.

B. Expanding Your Skill

Read the questions below. Which ones could you probably answer with a dictionary? Write those questions on your paper.

1. Did you spell a word the right way when you wrote it?
2. What are the uses of potatoes?
3. How many parts (syllables) does the word *potato* have?
4. Where are most of the dairy farms in the United States?
5. What is the right way to say the word *gross*?
6. What is okra?
7. How much does a quart of milk cost?

C. Exploring Language

Read the words below. Choose two of the words. On your paper, write a question about each word that can be answered with a dictionary. Trade questions with a classmate. Read the two questions you now have. Then find the answers in a dictionary.

potato   sugar   milk   cheese   grocery   flour

D. Expressing Yourself

Choose one of these things.

1. Play an ABC-order game with some of your classmates. For this game, imagine that the dictionary is made up of three parts like this:

Part 1	Part 2	Part 3
A - G	**H - P**	**Q - Z**

Now take turns reading the words below. For each word, one person tells the part of the dictionary it could be found in—1, 2, or 3. The next person then tells another word that fits in the same part of the dictionary.

boat   apple   print   hot   race   cage
job   sit   late   net   dress wet

2. Work in groups of four to "act" like a dictionary. The first person chooses a new word from a story and **says** the word. The second person **spells** the word out loud and shows it written on a strip of paper. The third person **tells the meaning** of the word. The fourth person **says each part**, or syllable, of the word and shows the parts written on a strip of paper.

UNIT 7
From Flour to Bread

(A) Some bread is baked at home, but most is made in a bread factory. (B) A bread factory is called a bakery. (C) Many thousands of loaves of bread can be made there in a single night.

(D) The first step in making bread is to make the flour into dough. (E) Water, yeast, vitamins, and other ingredients are mixed with the flour. (F) This is done in a giant mixing machine. (G) The machine tosses and mixes the dough until it is smooth.

(H) The dough is carried to a divider. (I) Here it is cut into pieces of the same weight. (J) Each piece of dough must be just the right weight for a loaf of bread. (K) The dough is shaped into loaf form and sent to the oven.

(L) The oven in a modern bakery is as large as a house. (M) It looks like a large tunnel. (N) The unbaked bread goes in at one end. (O) It comes out at the other end baked to a golden brown. (P) Many loaves of bread are baked at the same time.

(Q) After the loaves are cooled, they are sliced by sharp knives. (R) A moving belt carries the sliced loaves to the wrapping machine. (S) The machine wraps wax paper or plastic wrapping around each loaf and folds the wrapping at the ends. (T) The ends are pressed against hot plates. (U) The heat melts the wrapping a bit, and this makes the folded ends stick together.

(V) The fresh loaves of bread are loaded onto trucks. (W) The bread is hurried to the store near your home. (X) Not a single hand has touched the bread before you unwrap it for use.

UNIT 7
From Flour to Bread

1. What is a bread factory called?
   Sentence   (A)   (B)   (C)

2. Is making the flour into dough the last step?
   Sentence   (C)   (D)   (E)

3. In what are all the ingredients mixed?
   Sentence   (E)   (F)   (G)

4. Where is the dough carried?
   Sentence   (H)   (I)   (J)

5. Must each piece of dough be the right weight for a loaf?
   Sentence   (J)   (K)   (L)

6. Where does the unbaked bread go into the oven?
   Sentence   (M)   (N)   (O)

7. Is only one loaf of bread baked at a time?
   Sentence   (O)   (P)   (Q)

8. How does the sliced bread get to the wrapping machine?
   Sentence   (Q)   (R)   (S)

9. What causes the folded ends of the paper to stick together?
   Sentence   (S)   (T)   (U)

10. Where do trucks take the fresh loaves of bread?
    Sentence   (V)   (W)   (X)

(A) A fish is an animal that lives in the water. (B) It has a bone that lies in its back. (C) This is called a backbone. (D) A fish breathes through openings in the sides of its head called gills. (E) A fish is covered with scales rather than skin. (F) Instead of legs, it has fins, which help the fish move.

(G) There are two main groups of fish. (H) They are the saltwater fish and the freshwater fish. (I) Fish which live in the salty ocean are called saltwater fish. (J) Very often saltwater fish are blue-green in color, much like the ocean water. (K) Fish that come from rivers and lakes where the water is without salt are called freshwater fish.

(L) A third important group of sea animals is the shellfish. (M) The shellfish are not really fish, even though their name has the word "fish" in it. (N) To be real fish they would have to have backbones. (O) Shellfish live in the water, however, and are covered with a shell that protects their bodies. (P) Lobsters, crabs, shrimp, and oysters belong to the shellfish family.

(Q) There are many ways to catch fish. (R) Most fish are caught in large nets. (S) Fish may also be caught with traps. (T) Many fish are hooked and brought in on fishing lines that are dropped from boats or docks.

(U) Some of the fish that are caught are sold fresh. (V) Some are canned, frozen, or dried. (W) Any way they are served, fish make a tasty dish.

1. Does a fish have a bone in its back?
    Sentence   (A)   (B)   (C)

2. How does a fish breathe?
    Sentence   (C)   (D)   (E)

3. What does a fish have instead of skin?
    Sentence   (E)   (F)   (G)

4. How many groups of fish are there?
    Sentence   (G)   (H)   (I)

5. Are saltwater fish often the color of the ocean?
    Sentence   (J)   (K)   (L)

6. Are shellfish real fish?
    Sentence   (L)   (M)   (N)

7. What do all real fish have?
    Sentence   (N)   (O)   (P)

8. Are crabs shellfish?
    Sentence   (P)   (Q)   (R)

9. How are most fish caught?
    Sentence   (R)   (S)   (T)

10. Are many fish caught with hooks and lines?
    Sentence   (T)   (U)   (V)

(**A**) Fruits are parts of plants that always have one or more seeds. (**B**) They are the parts of the plants that come from the flower. (**C**) When the flower or blossom dies, the fruits and the seeds begin to grow. (**D**) Some fruits, such as the orange, have seeds scattered through them. (**E**) Other fruits, such as the peach, have just one seed called a pit or stone. (**F**) Still other fruits, such as the apple, have seeds in a core or center.

(**G**) There are three important groups of fruits. (**H**) One group is known as the "hot-country fruits." (**I**) The banana and pineapple belong to this group. (**J**) A second group is called the "warm-country fruits." (**K**) Oranges, lemons, and grapefruit belong to this group. (**L**) Sometimes they are called citrus fruits. (**M**) The third group is called "cool-country fruits." (**N**) Apples, pears, peaches, and many kinds of berries are in this group.

(**O**) Fruits grow on trees, bushes, and vines. (**P**) Apples and peaches grow on trees. (**Q**) Blueberries and many other berries grow on bushes. (**R**) Watermelons grow on vines. (**S**) Some fruit plants grow for many years. (**T**) Others live for only a year.

(**U**) People like fruit fresh, frozen, and canned. (**V**) Many people like dried fruit, that is, fruit with the juice taken out. (**W**) Fruit juice is a favorite of many people. (**X**) Orange juice and lemonade are two of the most popular fruit juices. (**Y**) One way or other, fruits are favorites of people all over the world.

1. Does a fruit always have at least one seed?
    Sentence   **(A)**   **(B)**   **(C)**

2. Does a peach have more than one seed?
    Sentence   **(C)**   **(D)**   **(E)**

3. Where are the seeds of the apple found?
    Sentence   **(E)**   **(F)**   **(G)**

4. Is the banana a "hot-country fruit"?
    Sentence   **(G)**   **(H)**   **(I)**

5. Do "warm-country fruits" have another name?
    Sentence   **(J)**   **(K)**   **(L)**

6. Is the pear a "cool-country fruit"?
    Sentence   **(M)**   **(N)**   **(O)**

7. Do peaches grow on trees?
    Sentence   **(O)**   **(P)**   **(Q)**

8. Do watermelons grow on vines?
    Sentence   **(Q)**   **(R)**   **(S)**

9. What are dried fruits?
    Sentence   **(T)**   **(U)**   **(V)**

10. Is lemonade liked by many people?
    Sentence   **(W)**   **(X)**   **(Y)**

(**A**) Chickens, turkeys, and ducks are birds known as poultry. (**B**) Another name for poultry is fowl. (**C**) A farmer who raises fowl to sell is called a poultry farmer. (**D**) A poultry farmer may raise different kinds or only one kind of fowl.

(**E**) Chickens are the birds most often served at tables. (**F**) More chickens are raised than either turkeys or ducks. (**G**) Chickens are raised for both their meat and their eggs.

(**H**) When the chickens raised for meat are large enough, they are sent to a packing plant and killed by machine. (**I**) Other machines then pluck off their feathers. (**J**) Still other machines clean the chickens.

(**K**) Some chickens are raised for their eggs. (**L**) Farmers gather the eggs soon after they are laid. (**M**) Eggs must be stored in a cool place to keep them from spoiling. (**N**) The eggs are sold soon after they are laid.

(**O**) Turkeys, like chickens, are also poultry. (**P**) Turkeys are raised in wire pens. (**Q**) They are fed and cared for much like chickens. (**R**) A full-grown turkey is larger than a chicken or a duck. (**S**) Turkey is now served at tables all year. (**T**) Many people eat one of these big birds on Thanksgiving Day.

(**U**) Ducks are also poultry. (**V**) They are more difficult to raise than chickens. (**W**) Ducks are water birds that can be raised on land. (**X**) Ducks are given soft food and plenty of drinking water. (**Y**) Many people enjoy the taste of duck. (**Z**) Ducks join chickens and turkeys as favorite table birds.

1. What name is given to a farmer who sells fowl?
   Sentence **(A)** **(B)** **(C)**

2. Which table birds are served most often?
   Sentence **(D)** **(E)** **(F)**

3. Are more chickens raised than ducks?
   Sentence **(F)** **(G)** **(H)**

4. When are chickens killed?
   Sentence **(H)** **(I)** **(J)**

5. How are chickens cleaned?
   Sentence **(J)** **(K)** **(L)**

6. Where are eggs stored to keep them from spoiling?
   Sentence **(L)** **(M)** **(N)**

7. Where are turkeys raised?
   Sentence **(N)** **(O)** **(P)**

8. Is a grown turkey larger than a chicken?
   Sentence **(Q)** **(R)** **(S)**

9. Are ducks easier to raise than chickens?
   Sentence **(T)** **(U)** **(V)**

10. Do ducks drink much water?
    Sentence **(W)** **(X)** **(Y)**

(A) One of the first wild animals ever tamed was the sheep. (B) Sheep have been raised in many parts of the world for thousands of years. (C) Long ago people found out that sheep could give both food and clothing. (D) They give meat to eat and wool for cloth. (E) People of some lands drink sheep's milk. (F) They also make cheese from the milk of sheep.

(G) Most sheep are raised in open country called the range. (H) They like to graze over dry pasture lands, eating grass and other plants. (I) Large numbers are raised in the West and the Southwest of our country. (J) Texas raises more than any other state. (K) The sheep live in large groups called flocks or herds. (L) Herds may have as many as two thousand sheep. (M) One sheep usually leads the herd. (N) Most often the leader is a male sheep, called a ram.

(O) A person who cares for sheep is called a shepherd. (P) A shepherd often has a sheepdog as a helper. (Q) The dog keeps the sheep together by circling them. (R) It barks and nips at their heels if they try to wander away. (S) The sheepdog also helps protect the sheep from wild animals.

(T) When sheep are three months old, they are heavy enough to be sent to market. (U) Meat from sheep that are less than a year old is called lamb. (V) Meat from older sheep is called mutton. (W) Lamb is more tender than mutton. (X) Most people in our country like the flavor of lamb better than mutton.

1. For how many years have sheep been raised?
   Sentence   (A)   (B)   (C)

2. What do we make from wool?
   Sentence   (C)   (D)   (E)

3. Can cheese be made from the milk of sheep?
   Sentence   (E)   (F)   (G)

4. What do sheep eat?
   Sentence   (H)   (I)   (J)

5. Do sheep live in flocks?
   Sentence   (J)   (K)   (L)

6. Which sheep usually leads the flock?
   Sentence   (L)   (M)   (N)

7. What person takes care of the sheep?
   Sentence   (O)   (P)   (Q)

8. Who helps to protect the sheep from wild animals?
   Sentence   (Q)   (R)   (S)

9. Is mutton the meat from older sheep?
   Sentence   (T)   (U)   (V)

10. Is lamb more tender than mutton?
    Sentence   (V)   (W)   (X)

UNIT 12
Sandwiches

(A) People in the United States eat about 300 million sandwiches a day. (B) That is more than one sandwich a day for each person. (C) Most people eat sandwiches for lunch. (D) But sandwiches may be eaten at any time of the day or night.

(E) A sandwich is made of something tasty placed between two slices of bread. (F) Or sometimes only one slice of bread is used. (G) Peanut butter, jelly, tomatoes, lettuce, meats, cheeses, and hard-cooked eggs are favorite sandwich fillings.

(H) Sandwiches are not a new invention. (I) Long ago the Hebrew people made a mixture of chopped green plants, apples, nuts, and honey. (J) They spread this on their special bread or matzoh. (K) The Romans ate meat on bread. (L) French farmers carried pieces of black bread filled with meat out into the fields.

(M) The sandwich got its name in England about two hundred years ago from the Earl of Sandwich. (N) The Earl did not want to take time off from playing a game, so he ordered a few slices of cold beef to be put between slices of bread. (O) It was handy to eat the beef in this way. (P) No knife or fork was needed. (Q) In a few years, everyone in England was eating "sandwiches."

(R) Sandwiches are now known all over the world. (S) To stay fresh, sandwiches are often covered by plastic wrap or put in special sandwich bags. (T) Sandwiches are carried to school or work in brown paper bags or in lunch boxes. (U) Sandwiches are carried to picnics in large baskets or coolers. (V) Tiny sandwiches of different shapes are often served at fancy parties.

1. When do most people eat sandwiches?
    Sentence   **(B)**   **(C)**   **(D)**

2. Is one slice of bread ever used?
    Sentence   **(D)**   **(E)**   **(F)**

3. Are sandwiches a new kind of food?
    Sentence   **(G)**   **(H)**   **(I)**

4. Who made sandwiches with chopped plants, apples, nuts, and honey?
    Sentence   **(I)**   **(J)**   **(K)**

5. Who made sandwiches with black bread?
    Sentence   **(K)**   **(L)**   **(M)**

6. Where did the sandwich get its name?
    Sentence   **(M)**   **(N)**   **(O)**

7. Did the Earl of Sandwich need a fork?
    Sentence   **(P)**   **(Q)**   **(R)**

8. Are sandwiches known only in England?
    Sentence   **(Q)**   **(R)**   **(S)**

9. How are sandwiches carried to school or work?
    Sentence   **(S)**   **(T)**   **(U)**

10. Are sandwiches also taken to picnics?
    Sentence   **(T)**   **(U)**   **(V)**

You have been reading stories about different things to eat. You read for fun and to learn. When you read, you can also skim or scan the story. The following will tell you about skimming and scanning.

Skimming: When you want to read something quickly to get the main ideas, you skim it. You do not look for facts; you just read quickly to get the main ideas.

Scanning: When you know what facts or information you are looking for, you can scan the story. You do not have to look for the main ideas. To scan, you move your eyes quickly over the page until you find what you want.

A. Exercising Your Skill

Think about what **skimming** means and what **scanning** means. Write the following sentences on your paper and fill in the blanks.

1. You can _____ a story when you want to get the main ideas.
2. You do not have to look for _____ when you skim.
3. You can _____ a story when you know the facts or information you are looking for.
4. You do not have to look for the _____ when you scan.

B. Expanding Your Skill

Read the following questions. Work with a partner. Imagine that you are reading a magazine story about a famous actor. Talk about whether you would skim or scan to answer each question.

1. What was the name of the actor?
2. When was the actor born?
3. What help did the young actor get?
4. What was the name of the actor's most popular TV show?
5. What does the story say about how hard the actor works?

C. Exploring Language

1. Work with a group of classmates. Skim the following story. Each person in the group writes its main idea. See how long it takes each person to find the main idea.

    Most cows give about twelve quarts of milk a day. Today farmers use two ways to milk cows: by hand and by machine. Farmers with only a few cows milk them by hand. On large dairy farms, milking machines are used. These machines pump warm milk from the cows' milk bags into pails.

2. With the same group of classmates, scan the following story. See how long it takes your group to find the answers to these questions:

    a. How does milk leave farms?

    b. Where does it go next?

    c. What happens to the milk at the plant?

    Every day milk is taken from the farm in big tank trunks. The milk is taken to a milk plant. The milk plant is sometimes called a creamery. Here, people smell, taste, and test the milk. This is to make sure that the milk is safe to drink.

D. Expressing Yourself

Choose one of these things.

1. Choose a story in a school book. Write three questions about the story that can be answered by scanning. Work with a partner. See how fast you can find the answers to each other's questions by scanning.

2. Write a short story about an animal. Tell at least three facts, such as what color, size, or shape the animal is and how it moves. Exchange papers with a partner. Skim your partner's story to find out what it is about. Scan the story to find out three facts. Write the things you found out.

UNIT 13
Beef Cattle

(A) Cattle are raised for both their meat and their milk. (B) The meat of cattle is called beef. (C) We eat more beef than any other meat. (D) The cattle which give us meat are known as beef cattle. (E) Cattle that give us milk are called dairy cattle.

(F) Beef cattle are raised on large farms known as ranches. (G) A number of cattle raised together is a herd. (H) Herds of cattle feed on grazing land. (I) They eat the grass and are fed hay. (J) When the cattle are ready for market, they are sent to a stockyard.

(K) A stockyard is a place where animals are kept until they are sold. (L) In the stockyards the cattle are fattened on corn and other food. (M) Cornfed cattle give the highest quality beef and veal. (N) The meat from young cattle, called calves, is known as veal. (O) Buyers visit the stockyards and choose the animals they want to buy. (P) Buyers know how to judge the quality of meat in every animal.

(Q) From the stockyards the cattle are sent to a packing plant in trains and trucks. (R) In the packing plant the animals are killed. (S) Some of the meat is put into cans but most is kept fresh. (T) The fresh meat is shipped in cool railroad cars to markets and stores.

(U) At the stores the meat is cut into smaller pieces. (V) Most of the meat is kept in a cool room in the back of the store. (W) Some of the meat is kept in a glass showcase, so that people can see what they are buying.

1. Why are cattle raised?
    Sentence   (A)   (B)   (C)

2. What are the cattle called that give us meat?
    Sentence   (C)   (D)   (E)

3. Where are beef cattle raised?
    Sentence   (F)   (G)   (H)

4. When are cattle sent to the stockyard?
    Sentence   (I)   (J)   (K)

5. What is a stockyard?
    Sentence   (K)   (L)   (M)

6. What do we call the meat from calves?
    Sentence   (M)   (N)   (O)

7. What skill does a cattle buyer have?
    Sentence   (O)   (P)   (Q)

8. How much meat is kept fresh?
    Sentence   (Q)   (R)   (S)

9. Where is the meat cut into smaller pieces?
    Sentence   (S)   (T)   (U)

10. Why is some meat placed in a glass showcase?
    Sentence   (U)   (V)   (W)

(A) The North American lobster is a shellfish. (B) It looks like a beetle about one foot long. (C) It weighs a pound or more when full-grown. (D) The lobster is entirely covered by a tough shell. (E) The meat inside the shell is the most highly prized seafood in America.

(F) The North American lobster can be found only in the cool waters of the western Atlantic. (G) It lives in the water along the entire east coast from North Carolina to Labrador. (H) The largest numbers are found off the coast of Maine and Canada. (I) Other types of lobsters are found in other waters. (J) But the North American lobster is the favorite of seafood lovers.

(K) The lobster is caught in traps called pots. (L) These are marked with a buoy. (M) A buoy is a float that bears the markings of the owner. (N) Care must be taken when getting the lobster out of the pot. (O) A person could easily be bitten. (P) The lobster has two powerful claws that can snap off a finger.

(Q) Once the lobster is caught, its catcher puts a peg in its claws. (R) The peg makes it impossible for the lobster to open its claws. (S) Then it cannot bite and cannot eat the smaller lobsters.

(T) Sometimes the lobster is cooked in boiling water; often it is steamed or broiled. (U) It is kept in the water until its dark green shell turns bright red. (V) Then it is ready for the table. (W) It is most tasty when served with melted butter.

(X) Sometimes more than one lobster is caught in the same pot. (Y) Lobster catchers tell you to examine your pots often. (Z) They warn, "If you do not, you will find only one lobster left—the biggest."

UNIT 14
The Amazing Lobster

1. Is lobster meat highly prized?
   Sentence **(D)** **(E)** **(F)**

2. On which coast can the North American lobsters be found?
   Sentence **(G)** **(H)** **(I)**

3. Where are most North American lobsters located?
   Sentence **(H)** **(I)** **(J)**

4. Is any type of lobster preferred?
   Sentence **(I)** **(J)** **(K)**

5. How is the lobster caught?
   Sentence **(J)** **(K)** **(L)**

6. Why must a lobster catcher be careful?
   Sentence **(M)** **(N)** **(O)**

7. What does the peg do to the claws?
   Sentence **(P)** **(Q)** **(R)**

8. In which kind of water is the lobster cooked?
   Sentence **(S)** **(T)** **(U)**

9. What makes the lobster most tasty?
   Sentence **(V)** **(W)** **(X)**

10. Why do lobster catchers tell you to examine your pots often?
    Sentence **(X)** **(Y)** **(Z)**

(**A**) All green plants make their own food. (**B**) Only a part of the food that a plant makes is needed to make the plant grow. (**C**) Much of the unused food is stored in some part of the plant. (**D**) The part of the plant where food is stored is the part we eat. (**E**) This may be the seed, the leaf, the stem, the root, or even the flower.

(**F**) The seeds of some plants are eaten as vegetables. (**G**) When we eat corn, we are eating the seeds of a plant. (**H**) When we eat fresh beans, we are eating both the seeds and their containers, called pods. (**I**) If we eat baked beans, we are eating only the seeds that have been taken from the pods.

(**J**) The leaves of some plants are also eaten as vegetables. (**K**) When we eat lettuce or spinach, we are eating the leaves of plants. (**L**) We also eat plant stems. (**M**) We do this when we eat celery and asparagus. (**N**) These two vegetables store food in their stems.

(**O**) There are many plants whose roots we eat. (**P**) The carrots, beets, and sweet potatoes we eat are the roots of plants. (**Q**) White potatoes are not really roots. (**R**) A white potato is just the swollen end of an underground stem.

(**S**) Sometimes we even eat the flowers of plants. (**T**) When we eat cauliflower, we are eating flowers.

(**U**) It seems strange to think that we eat leaves, stems, roots, seeds, and flowers. (**V**) Yet, when we eat vegetables that is exactly what we are doing. (**W**) Vegetables, we must remember, are parts of plants.

1. Do all green plants make their own food?

   Sentence   **(A)**   **(B)**   **(C)**

2. Do plants store their unused food?

   Sentence   **(C)**   **(D)**   **(E)**

3. Is corn the seed of a plant?

   Sentence   **(E)**   **(F)**   **(G)**

4. When we eat fresh beans, do we eat the pods?

   Sentence   **(G)**   **(H)**   **(I)**

5. When we eat baked beans, do we eat the pods?

   Sentence   **(I)**   **(J)**   **(K)**

6. Are lettuce and spinach the leaves of plants?

   Sentence   **(K)**   **(L)**   **(M)**

7. Does celery store food in its stems?

   Sentence   **(M)**   **(N)**   **(O)**

8. What part of the plant is the white potato?

   Sentence   **(P)**   **(Q)**   **(R)**

9. Can you name a flower eaten by people?

   Sentence   **(S)**   **(T)**   **(U)**

10. What are vegetables?

    Sentence   **(U)**   **(V)**   **(W)**

UNIT 16
Clothing Fashions

(A) The way that most people dress at any period of history is the fashion of that time. (B) Clothing fashions have changed through the years. (C) The styles of today are much different from those of long ago.

(D) The first clothing was made to protect people from weather. (E) It was also made to give people better looks. (F) Animal skins made warm and nice-looking coverings for people. (G) Later on, cloth was wrapped loosely around the body. (H) The cloth was not fitted to the shape of the body.

(I) A big change in fashion came in the 1400s and 1500s. (J) People began wearing fitted clothes. (K) High-heeled shoes and fancy clothing made of silk and velvet were the fashion. (L) The leaders of countries usually set the styles of the day.

(M) In the 1600s and 1700s, people wore very beautiful clothing. (N) The clothing was not at all comfortable, though. (O) Sometimes its wearers found it difficult to move. (P) The clothes of this period were heavy, stiff, and tight-fitting.

(Q) Clothing began to be more comfortable in the 1800s. (R) Fashions became somewhat loose and flowing. (S) The lighter materials that were used gave clothes a softer look. (T) Most of the footwear was flat.

(U) In the 1900s, another big change in fashion came about. (V) Clothing began to be made in factories at less cost. (W) More people were able to buy clothes that were in style. (X) The clothes allowed people to move about more freely than ever before. (Y) Today's fashions have become both beautiful and comfortable.

1. Are the fashions of today very different from those of long ago?
   Sentence   (A)   (B)   (C)

2. Were animal skins used to protect people from cold?
   Sentence   (D)   (E)   (F)

3. Was cloth wrapped around the body tightly or loosely?
   Sentence   (G)   (H)   (I)

4. Were high-heeled shoes in style in the 1400s?
   Sentence   (I)   (J)   (K)

5. Who set the fashions of the day?
   Sentence   (K)   (L)   (M)

6. Did people wear beautiful clothing in the 1700s?
   Sentence   (M)   (N)   (O)

7. Could the wearers of this clothing move about easily?
   Sentence   (O)   (P)   (Q)

8. What were most of the shoes like in the 1800s?
   Sentence   (R)   (S)   (T)

9. When did another big change in fashion come about?
   Sentence   (T)   (U)   (V)

10. Were more people able to buy factory-made clothes?
    Sentence   (U)   (V)   (W)

UNIT 17
Clothes from Wool

(**A**) Sheep are raised by farmers for their fine coats of wool. (**B**) In the winter the wool keeps the sheep warm. (**C**) As the weather becomes warmer, sheep have no need for their warm overcoats. (**D**) The wool can then be clipped from them.

(**E**) Cutting off a sheep's wool is called shearing a sheep. (**F**) Shearing does not hurt the animal any more than it hurts us to have our hair cut. (**G**) Large clippers, called shears, clip the wool from the animal. (**H**) Electric shears are used by some people in place of hand shears. (**I**) The electric clippers do the job faster.

(**J**) Whenever possible, the wool is clipped from the sheep in one piece. (**K**) Baby sheep, called lambs, are sheared as well as the "grown-ups." (**L**) The wool from lambs is soft and fine. (**M**) It sells for a high price. (**N**) Wool, once it is cut from an animal, is called fleece. (**O**) Fleece is usually cut from an animal once a year. (**P**) After the shearing, the fleeces are sent to the woolen mills.

(**Q**) At the woolen mills the fleeces are torn apart and sorted. (**R**) The high-grade wool is kept in one stack. (**S**) The poorer quality wool is kept in another. (**T**) The wool is washed until it is snowy white, after which it is dried and dyed. (**U**) It is then pulled into long strands. (**V**) From these strands thread is made. (**W**) The thread, in turn, is made into cloth.

(**X**) Sheep are among the most valuable of our animals. (**Y**) Not only do sheep give us meat, but they also provide us with cloth to make into woolen clothes.

1. How does wool help sheep in the winter?
    Sentence   **(A)**   **(B)**   **(C)**

2. Does shearing a sheep hurt the animal?
    Sentence   **(D)**   **(E)**   **(F)**

3. Why are electric shears sometimes used?
    Sentence   **(G)**   **(H)**   **(I)**

4. Are baby sheep ever sheared?
    Sentence   **(J)**   **(K)**   **(L)**

5. Why does lamb's wool sell for a high price?
    Sentence   **(L)**   **(M)**   **(N)**

6. What is wool called once it is sheared from the sheep?
    Sentence   **(N)**   **(O)**   **(P)**

7. Where is the wool sent after shearing?
    Sentence   **(P)**   **(Q)**   **(R)**

8. Where is the high-grade wool placed?
    Sentence   **(Q)**   **(R)**   **(S)**

9. Does the wool need to be washed?
    Sentence   **(T)**   **(U)**   **(V)**

10. Why are sheep considered such helpful animals?
    Sentence   **(W)**   **(X)**   **(Y)**

UNIT 18
Clothes from a Bird

(A) Did you know that geese are water birds? (B) Geese are very much like ducks and swans. (C) Male geese are called ganders, females are called geese, and babies are called goslings.

(D) Geese are important to people. (E) Goose eggs and meat have been used as food for ages. (F) The hard parts of their feathers were once used as pens for writing. (G) Their feathers were also used on fancy hats. (H) Geese have been used even to guard farms. (I) They honk and hiss and scare strangers away.

(J) Now goose down is used often by people for warmth. (K) Goose down is soft, fluffy goose feathers. (L) These feathers grow close to the bird's body. (M) Goose down has no hard parts. (N) It is also very light in weight. (O) Down keeps geese and people warm.

(P) Goose down can be carefully pulled out, or plucked, from live geese. (Q) It can be taken several times a year from the same bird. (R) Down is then used in clothing and other coverings for light-weight warmth. (S) It is used in the lining of coats, jackets, and vests. (T) It is also used in bed coverings and sleeping bags.

(U) Coats lined with down are popular in cold weather. (V) Clothing lined with down costs more than clothing lined with most other materials. (W) Down clothing also has to be cleaned in a special way. (X) Many people buy down clothing anyway because of its warmth and comfort.

1. Geese are like what other birds?
   Sentence   **(A)**   **(B)**   **(C)**

2. Do people eat goose eggs?
   Sentence   **(C)**   **(D)**   **(E)**

3. Were goose feathers ever used on hats?
   Sentence   **(E)**   **(F)**   **(G)**

4. Have geese ever been used to guard farms?
   Sentence   **(H)**   **(I)**   **(J)**

5. What is goose down?
   Sentence   **(K)**   **(L)**   **(M)**

6. Does goose down have any hard parts?
   Sentence   **(M)**   **(N)**   **(O)**

7. Why is goose down useful?
   Sentence   **(O)**   **(P)**   **(Q)**

8. Why is down used in clothing?
   Sentence   **(Q)**   **(R)**   **(S)**

9. Does clothing lined with down cost more?
   Sentence   **(T)**   **(U)**   **(V)**

10. Why do many people buy down clothing?
    Sentence   **(V)**   **(W)**   **(X)**

UNIT 19
Clothes from a Worm

(**A**) Long, long ago only the people of China knew the secret of making silk. (**B**) The Chinese guarded their secret for a long time, but finally it leaked out. (**C**) The world was surprised to learn that the Chinese got their silk from a worm! (**D**) The silk that the Chinese made into cloth came from the body of an insect—the silkworm.

(**E**) Today silk making is carried on in many countries of the world. (**F**) It is not an easy job. (**G**) Silkworms are difficult to raise. (**H**) They do not like noise. (**I**) They do not like cold weather. (**J**) Above all, silkworms are fussy eaters. (**K**) Only one food will satisfy them, the leaves of the mulberry tree.

(**L**) After the silkworm is four or five weeks old, it is fully grown. (**M**) Then it is ready to spin its cocoon. (**N**) A cocoon is a sort of house in which the worm plans to sleep. (**O**) The cocoon is made from a silk thread that comes out of the worm's body in a long piece. (**P**) The worm forms a round, white house by spinning this thread around itself.

(**Q**) Cocoons are sent to a silk factory to be made into cloth. (**R**) At the factory the cocoons are put into warm water to soften the fibers. (**S**) Workers unwind the long, thin threads from the cocoons. (**T**) Fibers from four or more cocoons are twisted together to form a silk thread. (**U**) The thread is then made into cloth.

1. Did people other than the Chinese learn the secret of silk making?
   Sentence   (A)   (B)   (C)

2. Where is silk made today?
   Sentence   (C)   (D)   (E)

3. Do silkworms like noise?
   Sentence   (F)   (G)   (H)

4. Do silkworms like cold weather?
   Sentence   (H)   (I)   (J)

5. What food do silkworms eat?
   Sentence   (J)   (K)   (L)

6. Do silkworms take long to grow?
   Sentence   (L)   (M)   (N)

7. Why does the silkworm make a cocoon?
   Sentence   (M)   (N)   (O)

8. What color is a cocoon?
   Sentence   (O)   (P)   (Q)

9. Why are cocoons put into warm water?
   Sentence   (Q)   (R)   (S)

10. Who unwinds the silk thread from the cocoons?
    Sentence   (S)   (T)   (U)

You have been reading about different kinds of food and clothing. Menus and store signs also give information about food and clothing.

A. Exercising Your Skill

Work with a classmate. Tell or list on paper all the kinds of information you find on a menu in a restaurant or on the signs in supermarkets.

B. Expanding Your Skill

Look at the menu below. It is written in three parts, or columns. On your paper, write in your own words the kinds of information found in each of the three columns.

MENU

(1)	(2)	(3)
Chicken Treat	baked chicken carrots baked potato	$5.00
Stew for You	beef stew mixed salad	$4.25
Veggie-Roll	vegetables in pocket bread green salad	$3.75
Catch-of-the-Day	baked tuna mixed vegetables mashed potatoes	$5.00

all served with wheat roll and butter

C. Exploring Language

Look at this floor sign, or directory, from a department store.

First Floor	greeting cards, books, jewelry, shoes
Second Floor	suits, slacks, dresses, coats, jackets, sweaters
Third Floor	baby's and children's clothes, sheets, pillowcases, towels

On your paper, write each question number and then answer the questions.

1. What two gifts could you buy for a birthday gift for your aunt?
2. On which floor would you buy a gift for your brother? What would you buy?
3. On which floor would you look for a gift for yourself? What would you buy?

D. Expressing Yourself

Choose one of these things.

1. On your paper, draw a plan of your bedroom or a bedroom you would like to have. Divide it into four parts and label the parts A, B, C, and D. Draw some things that are in each part, such as a book, a pair of slippers, or a blanket. Then ask a classmate which part of the room he or she would look in for each thing.

2. Put together a "Hunt It Out" game. Hide things in different places. Write clues for finding the things on slips of paper. Put the clues in a box. Have players take slips of paper and follow the clues. When something is found, another slip can be taken. See who can find the most things in fifteen minutes.

UNIT 20
Clothes from Cotton

(**A**) Cotton is the most widely used of all materials made into clothes. (**B**) More than half of all the people in the world wear clothes made from the cotton plant. (**C**) Many of our shirts, dresses, socks, and handkerchiefs are made from cotton.

(**D**) The flowers of the cotton plant are white when they first open. (**E**) Soon the flowers fall off the plant and a green seed ball is left. (**F**) The seed ball is called a boll. (**G**) When the cotton boll is ripe, it bursts open and shows a bunch of puffy white fibers. (**H**) It is from this white fiber that cotton cloth is made.

(**I**) On small farms most of the cotton is picked by hand. (**J**) Pickers gather the cotton in large bags. (**K**) This is not easy. (**L**) A picker tries to get only the cotton and not to collect leaves and stems.

(**M**) Machines are used to pick cotton on larger farms. (**N**) Machines make the job of picking cotton easier, but they are costly to buy. (**O**) Then, too, machines collect the stems and leaves as well as the cotton.

(**P**) The picked cotton is weighed and emptied into a wagon. (**Q**) It is then sent to a cotton mill. (**R**) There the seeds are taken out of the cotton. (**S**) The cotton is pressed into bales so that it can be shipped more easily. (**T**) Large bales of cotton often weigh many hundreds of pounds.

(**U**) At the cotton mill the fibers are pulled out into long strands. (**V**) Cotton thread is made from these strands. (**W**) The thread is woven into cloth.

1. How many people wear clothes made of cotton?
   Sentence   **(A)**   **(B)**   **(C)**

2. What clothes are made from cotton?
   Sentence   **(C)**   **(D)**   **(E)**

3. What is the seed ball called?
   Sentence   **(E)**   **(F)**   **(G)**

4. When does the seed ball burst open?
   Sentence   **(G)**   **(H)**   **(I)**

5. How is cotton picked on small farms?
   Sentence   **(I)**   **(J)**   **(K)**

6. How is cotton picked on large farms?
   Sentence   **(K)**   **(L)**   **(M)**

7. Are cotton-picking machines costly?
   Sentence   **(N)**   **(O)**   **(P)**

8. Why is cotton pressed into bales?
   Sentence   **(Q)**   **(R)**   **(S)**

9. How much does a bale of cotton weigh?
   Sentence   **(S)**   **(T)**   **(U)**

10. Where are the fibers pulled into strands?
    Sentence   **(U)**   **(V)**   **(W)**

UNIT 21
Clothes from Science

(A) People have learned to make cloth from fibers that are not produced by nature. (B) These fibers are called synthetic fibers and are made into thread. (C) The thread is woven into a synthetic cloth.

(D) For years people had looked for something to take the place of silk. (E) Silk was very costly, so not everyone could buy it. (F) Science found the answer in rayon. (G) Rayon is a cloth that is made from wood or cotton. (H) Rayon is lighter and cheaper than silk, and it is often used in shirts and dresses.

(I) Nylon is used to make many clothes. (J) Light and strong, it is used in stockings and underclothes. (K) It is a synthetic cloth made out of coal.

(L) The newest of the synthetic cloths are the polyesters. (M) These are made from oil. (N) Your suits, slacks, and coats may be made of polyester. (O) Polyester does not wrinkle. (P) Creases are put in by heat. (Q) These creases never disappear. (R) Polyester is a "cloth with a memory."

(S) It is strange when you think where your clothes may have come from. (T) They may have come from a giant tree. (U) They may have come from a lump of coal. (V) Or they may have once been a puddle of oil!

(W) Science is not through yet. (X) Scientists have made clothing from paper! (Y) Handsome clothes of paper are cheap, and when you are through with them, do not worry. (Z) You simply throw them away!

UNIT 21
Clothes from Science

1. Into what is the thread woven?
    Sentence   **(A)**   **(B)**   **(C)**

2. Did silk cost much money?
    Sentence   **(D)**   **(E)**   **(F)**

3. What is rayon made from?
    Sentence   **(G)**   **(H)**   **(I)**

4. What clothes may contain rayon?
    Sentence   **(H)**   **(I)**   **(J)**

5. What is nylon made from?
    Sentence   **(J)**   **(K)**   **(L)**

6. What are the latest of the synthetic cloths?
    Sentence   **(K)**   **(L)**   **(M)**

7. Is oil used to make any synthetic cloth?
    Sentence   **(M)**   **(N)**   **(O)**

8. Does polyester wrinkle?
    Sentence   **(O)**   **(P)**   **(Q)**

9. Do creases ever disappear in polyester?
    Sentence   **(Q)**   **(R)**   **(S)**

10. What new kind of clothing is both handsome and cheap?
    Sentence   **(W)**   **(X)**   **(Y)**

UNIT 22
Shelters for Living

(**A**) The houses in which we live are called shelters. (**B**) They shelter us from the cold winters and the hot summers. (**C**) During the winter they keep out the snow and the wind. (**D**) In the summer, shelters keep the hot sun from us. (**E**) When it rains, shelters keep us dry.

(**F**) Shelters help protect the things we own. (**G**) They keep our toys, books, clothes, and other things safe. (**H**) They keep insects and animals away from us. (**I**) Shelters give us a chance to be together with our families and friends. (**J**) They give us a place in which to eat, sleep, and play.

(**K**) Houses, which are the most important kinds of shelters, are different in many ways. (**L**) They are often made of many different materials. (**M**) Some houses are made of wood. (**N**) Some are made of brick or stone. (**O**) In others, all of these materials are used.

(**P**) Houses differ from one another in size. (**Q**) Some houses have only one room. (**R**) Most houses in our country have more than one room. (**S**) Large apartment houses found in cities have a great many rooms. (**T**) The rooms in which each family lives are called an apartment.

(**U**) Houses are different in the ways they are built. (**V**) Houses found in hot countries are often lightly built. (**W**) In places where it is very cold the houses are usually strong and warm. (**X**) In places where it is very wet much of the year, the houses are specially built to keep out the rain.

1. Are houses called shelters?
   Sentence   **(A)**   **(B)**   **(C)**

2. How do shelters help us in the summer?
   Sentence   **(C)**   **(D)**   **(E)**

3. How do shelters help us when it rains?
   Sentence   **(E)**   **(F)**   **(G)**

4. Do people sleep in shelters?
   Sentence   **(H)**   **(I)**   **(J)**

5. Are all houses made of the same materials?
   Sentence   **(K)**   **(L)**   **(M)**

6. Are houses all the same size?
   Sentence   **(N)**   **(O)**   **(P)**

7. Do most houses have more than one room?
   Sentence   **(P)**   **(Q)**   **(R)**

8. Do large apartment houses in cities have many rooms?
   Sentence   **(R)**   **(S)**   **(T)**

9. Are houses in hot countries often more lightly built?
   Sentence   **(T)**   **(U)**   **(V)**

10. Are houses in wet places built in a special way?
    Sentence   **(V)**   **(W)**   **(X)**

(A) Houses in our country are built of many different kinds of materials. (B) Among the best-liked materials are wood, stone, brick, and concrete. (C) The size of the house, the style, and the climate have a lot to do with the kinds of materials used.

(D) Wood is the material that is most often used for building houses. (E) It is easy to get and does not cost too much. (F) There is much wood still left in our country. (G) Wood can be cut into almost any shape or size. (H) Many different kinds of wood are used for many different parts of the house.

(I) Brick is another well-liked building material which all of us have seen. (J) Maybe your own house is made of brick. (K) Brick is strong and it lasts a long time. (L) It is rather easy to get. (M) Some brick comes from a red clay. (N) Brick of other colors can also be bought.

(O) Concrete blocks and stone make houses strong and pretty. (P) Concrete is made from cement. (Q) Concrete does not cost as much as stone. (R) Stone must be dug from the ground in a place called a quarry. (S) Slate is a stone that is sometimes used for roofs. (T) Sandstone is used for walls. (U) Limestone is used mainly for foundations.

(V) Glass is found in almost every house. (W) Often a single large window takes up half a wall or even more in some houses. (X) Even some bricks are now made of glass.

UNIT 23
Materials for Shelter

1. Are houses in our country all made of the same materials?
    Sentence   (A)   (B)   (C)

2. What material is used most often for building houses?
    Sentence   (C)   (D)   (E)

3. Does wood cost much money?
    Sentence   (E)   (F)   (G)

4. Can wood be cut into different shapes?
    Sentence   (G)   (H)   (I)

5. Does brick last long?
    Sentence   (J)   (K)   (L)

6. Is brick easy to get?
    Sentence   (L)   (M)   (N)

7. From what is concrete made?
    Sentence   (N)   (O)   (P)

8. Does concrete cost as much as stone?
    Sentence   (P)   (Q)   (R)

9. In what part of a house is slate used?
    Sentence   (S)   (T)   (U)

10. Are bricks ever made of glass?
    Sentence   (V)   (W)   (X)

UNIT 24
Building an Apartment House

(A) The people who build apartment houses must go through many different steps. (B) First, the owner must decide on the size and the place of the building.

(C) Then a special person called a planner takes over. (D) The planner looks at the owner's ideas to see if they obey building laws. (E) These laws were made by the city and state governments.

(F) There are many kinds of building laws. (G) One law says what sizes and types of buildings can be built in an area. (H) Another kind says what building materials can be used. (I) Other laws have to do with fire escapes, air, and lighting. (J) Still other laws have to do with elevators, air conditioning, heating, electric wiring, and water pipes.

(K) If the plans for the building follow all the laws, the planner sends out a notice to builders. (L) Different builders then offer their prices to the planner, and one builder is chosen.

(M) Special workers must also be hired. (N) They are painters, plumbers, frameworkers, and people who work with electricity.

(O) When work begins, the building will be put together in four steps. (P) The first step is the foundation. (Q) This supports, or holds up, the building from the bottom. (R) The second step is the frame. (S) This supports the building in the middle. (T) The third step includes the roof and outside and inside walls. (U) Walls close the building in and divide it into areas. (V) In the last step, the wiring, piping, heating and cooling systems, and elevators are put in the building.

1. What must the owner decide first?
    Sentence   (A)   (B)   (C)

2. What does the planner do?
    Sentence   (C)   (D)   (E)

3. Are there many kinds of building laws?
    Sentence   (E)   (F)   (G)

4. Are there laws about how big a building may be?
    Sentence   (G)   (H)   (I)

5. Are there laws about electric wiring?
    Sentence   (I)   (J)   (K)

6. To whom do builders offer their prices?
    Sentence   (L)   (M)   (N)

7. Do special workers need to be hired?
    Sentence   (M)   (N)   (O)

8. How many steps does it take to build a building?
    Sentence   (O)   (P)   (Q)

9. What does the foundation do?
    Sentence   (Q)   (R)   (S)

10. What do walls do?
    Sentence   (T)   (U)   (V)

(**A**) Just as tribes of long ago moved from place to place, many people of today travel and take their shelters with them. (**B**) Shelters that can be moved easily are tents, motor houses, campers, vans, trailers, and boats. (**C**) There are parks, campgrounds, and harbors that serve people who travel with their shelters.

(**D**) Tents come in different weights, sizes, shapes, colors, and materials. (**E**) Tents can be folded into small bundles. (**F**) Many tents are light enough to be carried on a person's back or on a bicycle. (**G**) Tents do not take up much room in a car or truck. (**H**) There are small pup tents and large umbrella tents with screened-in porches. (**I**) Tents are shelters that can be put up and taken down quickly.

(**J**) Motor houses, campers, and vans are shelters with motors and wheels. (**K**) They look something like buses on the outside. (**L**) Instead of having rows of seats inside, they have tables, chairs, stoves, sinks, beds, showers, and toilets.

(**M**) Trailers are long, narrow houses on wheels. (**N**) They are pulled behind cars. (**O**) They are usually made of metal. (**P**) Trailers may have as many as six rooms. (**Q**) Many parks and campgrounds have special hookups for trailers. (**R**) The trailers can be hooked up to get electricity and water.

(**S**) Some people live on boats all year long. (**T**) Boats that carry goods back and forth often have living spaces for families. (**U**) Sailors spend their days and nights aboard ships. (**V**) Many people own boats on which they live and travel. (**W**) These boats have cabins for eating and sleeping. (**X**) People can travel around the world while living on boats and ships.

UNIT 25
Moving Shelters

1. How are people of today like the tribes of long ago?
   Sentence   (**A**)   (**B**)   (**C**)

2. Can tents be folded up?
   Sentence   (**C**)   (**D**)   (**E**)

3. Do some tents have screened-in porches?
   Sentence   (**F**)   (**G**)   (**H**)

4. What do motor houses look like on the outside?
   Sentence   (**I**)   (**J**)   (**K**)

5. Are trailers short and wide?
   Sentence   (**K**)   (**L**)   (**M**)

6. What are trailers usually made of?
   Sentence   (**M**)   (**N**)   (**O**)

7. Are there parks and campgrounds with trailer hookups?
   Sentence   (**O**)   (**P**)   (**Q**)

8. Can the trailers get electricity and water?
   Sentence   (**Q**)   (**R**)   (**S**)

9. Do sailors live in moving shelters?
   Sentence   (**S**)   (**T**)   (**U**)

10. Why do boats have cabins?
    Sentence   (**V**)   (**W**)   (**X**)

Science is not through yet. Scientists have made clothing from paper! Handsome clothes of paper are cheap, and when you are through with them, do not worry. You simply throw them away!

A. Exercising Your Skill

The sentences above are from one of the stories you read. You learn about new things like paper clothing all the time. You get facts from books, television, newspapers, and magazines.

Work with a partner. Talk about the different kinds of books you have in school. Then list the different types of facts, or information, you can find in each book.

B. Expanding Your Skill

Below are four subjects you probably study in school. Write them as headings on your paper. Then read each question. On your paper, write the number of the question under the heading for the kind of book you would use to find the answer.

Reading	Science	Social Studies	Spelling
___	___	___	___
___	___	___	___

1. Why did the Pilgrims come to America?
2. Who wrote the first story that is in our class's reader?
3. At what temperature does water boil?
4. Who is the main character in the last story we read?
5. How are the words *bring, sing,* and *ring* alike?
6. When did George Washington become President?
7. What are the names of the planets in our solar system?
8. What happens in the story *Ramona Quimby, Age 8*?
9. What must you do when you add *ed* to stop?
10. Where is Lake Michigan located?

C. Exploring Language

Look at the list in the box. It tells what is in the first two chapters of a science book. Then, on your paper, write and finish the sentences below the box. Tell where you would look to find the information.

Chapter 1	**Seasons** ....Page	
	Fall 2	
	Winter 4	
	Spring..6	
	Summer...8	
Chapter 2	**Night and Day**	
	Light from the Sun......................10	
	The Sun and the Earth 13	
	The Moon and the Earth 16	

1. To find out about the different seasons, look at the chapter called

   _____ .

2. To find out what happens to plants and animals in the winter, turn to

   page _____ .

3. Facts about how the earth goes around the sun can be found in

   chapter _____ .

4. Facts about how the moon goes around the earth are in the part that

   begins on page _____ .

D. Expressing Yourself

Choose one of these things.

1. Write a store sign, or directory. Show where to find all your favorite things. List the floors of the store, and list the things found on each floor.

2. Work with one or two classmates. Use your science book to find a project, or experiment, that asks you to get some things together (such as a cardboard tube, some sand, and a bowl of water). Talk with your classmates about where you might find each of the things for the project.